LION OF AFRICA

Written by
MARY JENNIFER PAYNE

Illustrated by
LEO LINGAS

This story is set in 20th-century Africa. Each chapter ends with a non-fiction page that gives more information about South Africa, actual events and real people's lives at that time.

OXFORD
UNIVERSITY PRESS

NELSON ROLIHLAHLA MANDELA

REAL PEOPLE IN HISTORY

NELSON ROLIHLAHLA MANDELA (1918–): He fought for freedom on behalf of South Africa's black people.

F.W. DE KLERK (1936–): The president of South Africa who put an end to apartheid and changed the country forever.

WINNIE MANDELA (1936–): Nelson Mandela's second wife. She also fought for black people's rights.

FICTIONAL CHARACTERS

JOHN: A young prison guard who comes to learn a great deal about his country.

INGRID: John's mother. She believes things in South Africa should stay the way they are.

MANDISA: A young woman who is employed as a servant by John's family.

F.W. DE KLERK

WINNIE MANDELA

JOHN

INGRID

MANDISA

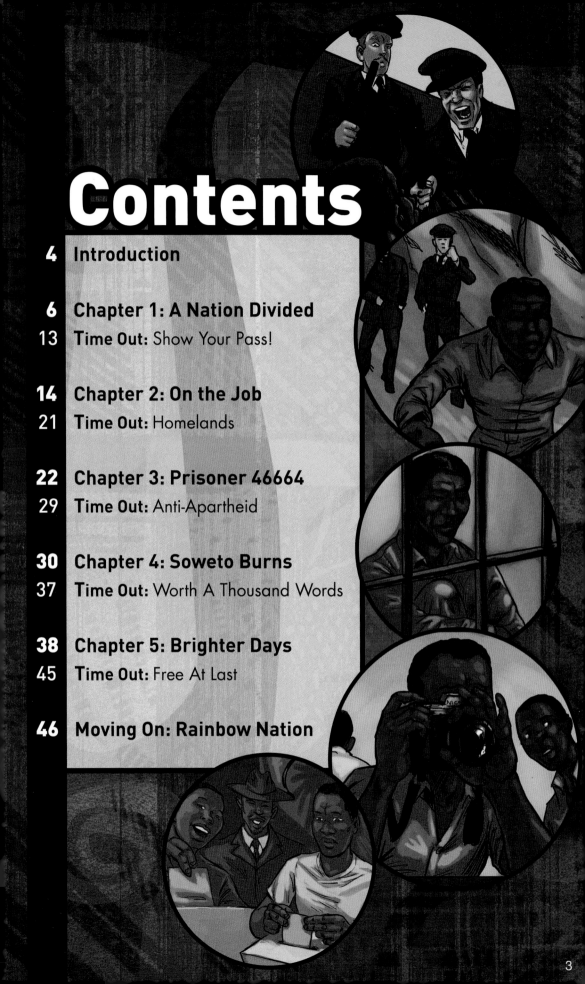

Contents

The Dutch were the first Europeans to colonise South Africa in the 16th century. The Dutch and their descendants – called Afrikaners – ruled South Africa. The British took over in the early 19th century.

The people of South Africa were made up of many racial and ethnic groups. There were native black peoples, whites of Dutch and British descent, Asians and people of mixed races.

Until 1994, South Africa practised apartheid. It was a system that discriminated against non-whites. Under apartheid, white people held all the power and much of the wealth. They ruled over black people, even though black people formed almost 80 per cent of the population. Non-whites were not allowed to vote. Their living conditions were much poorer.

1912	1918	1948	1960	1961
The African National Congress (ANC) is founded to promote rights for the black people of South Africa.	Nelson Mandela is born in the Transkei region of South Africa on 18 July.	The pro-white National Party comes to power. Its laws discriminate against the blacks.	South African police fire at black protesters in Sharpeville. Sixty-nine people die.	South Africa is expelled from the Commonwealth of Nations (former colonies of the British Empire).

Many people around the world rejected apartheid. Within South Africa, the African National Congress (ANC) protested against the system. It worked to gain equal rights for all South Africans.

South Africans march in the street.

One ANC leader became a symbol of the struggle for freedom and human rights. This story is about that leader – Nelson Mandela.

This story is set in an actual time in history, although some of the events are fictional. Real events during this period are shown on the timeline below.

1964 »	1976 »	1990 »	1993 »	1994 »
Mandela is leader of the ANC. He is sentenced to life in prison.	Police fire on young black protesters in Soweto, killing hundreds.	Mandela is released from prison after 27 years.	Nelson Mandela and President F. W. de Klerk share the Nobel Peace Prize.	South Africa holds its first multiracial elections. Mandela becomes the country's first black president.

9

SHOW YOUR PASS!

South African man holding passbook

Under apartheid, the cities and towns of South Africa were meant for whites only. Blacks in these areas had to carry passbooks. If they were caught without one, they could be arrested and sent into the countryside.

A passbook had a person's photograph, fingerprints and employer's name inside. Employers – who were of course white – could write what they thought of the person inside the passbook.

The people saw the passbook as a symbol of apartheid. They hated it. They felt their dignity had been taken away.

FOR 13 YEARS, MANDELA HAS BEEN IN SECTION B MINING THE LIME QUARRIES.

DID YOU KNOW WE GAVE MANDELA THE CHANCE TO GO FREE?

HE REFUSED!

WHY?

HE REFUSES TO LIVE IN THE BANTUSTANS — LAND THAT THE GOVERNMENT GAVE HIS PEOPLE.

THE PRISONERS ARE GIVEN SHOVELS AND PICKS TO BEGIN WORK.

WE'LL BE BACK WITH LUNCH AT NOON.

MAKE SURE THE PRISONERS WORK HARD!

HOMELANDS

In 1951, the South African government created several 'homelands' for black people to live in. These regions were called Bantustans. They were said to be the original homelands of black South Africans. It wasn't true of course.

Millions of black people were forced to move to the homelands. Life in these regions was extremely hard. Once they moved, they lost the right to live in South Africa even if they still worked there.

AFRICA

The idea behind the homelands was that, once all the black people had moved to them, the whites would have South Africa to themselves. For this reason, many blacks, including Nelson Mandela, refused to live in the Bantustans.

☐ **BANTUSTANS**

South Africa

ALL RIGHT THEN, LET ME TELL YOU A STORY INSTEAD.

"ON 21 MARCH 1960, A GROUP OF BLACK SOUTH AFRICANS FROM THE TOWNSHIP OF SHARPEVILLE GATHERED TOGETHER TO PROTEST AGAINST A TERRIBLE LAW."

"THE PEOPLE WERE ANGRY BECAUSE THEY HAD TO CARRY PASSBOOKS TO SHOW THEIR IDENTITY. THE POLICE CONFRONTED THEM."

DOWN WITH THE PASS LAWS!

"THE FATE OF SOUTH AFRICA CHANGED THAT DAY."

"BY THE END OF THAT DAY, NEARLY 70 PROTESTERS LAY DEAD, MANY OF THEM WOMEN AND CHILDREN. HUNDREDS WERE WOUNDED."

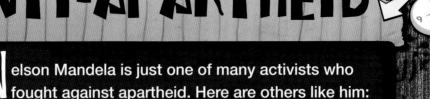

ANTI-APARTHEID

TIME OUT!

Nelson Mandela is just one of many activists who fought against apartheid. Here are others like him:

STEVE BIKO (1946–1977)

- Leader of the Black Consciousness Movement
- Followed a path of non-violence in his struggle against apartheid
- Suffered from a head injury in a prison cell and died from brain damage

NADINE GORDIMER (1923–)

- Wrote books on apartheid
- Became famous as an author worldwide
- Showed support for the black people of South Africa
- Won the Nobel Prize for Literature in 1991

DESMOND TUTU (1931–)

- Was Archbishop of Cape Town from 1986 to 1996
- Spoke out against apartheid all over the world
- Called for an end to the passbook laws
- Won the Nobel Peace Prize in 1984

MEANWHILE, IN JOHN'S HOME, THE SERVANT MANDISA SEES SOMETHING DISTURBING ON TELEVISION.

OH, NO! I HOPE MY FAMILY IS SAFE.

TODAY, SCHOOLCHILDREN IN SOWETO ARE PROTESTING AGAINST THE TEACHING OF THE AFRIKAANS LANGUAGE.

THE SCHOOLCHILDREN PROTEST PEACEFULLY.

NO MANDATORY AFRIKAANS

NO AFRIKAANS

N

KEE

THE POLICE, HOWEVER, ARE ANYTHING BUT PEACEFUL.

MANDISA'S COUSIN ANTOINETTE GOES TO SCHOOL IN SOWETO.

ANTOINETTE AND HER BROTHER HECTOR ARE IN THE MIDDLE OF THE RIOT.

ANTOINETTE!

HECTOR! OVER HERE!

HOW WILL WE GET HOME?

THE POLICE ARE EVERYWHERE!

THERE MUST BE ANOTHER WAY OUT OF HERE.

ANTOINETTE LEAVES HER BROTHER TO SEARCH FOR A WAY HOME THROUGH THE CHAOS.

YOU STAY HERE WHILE I LOOK FOR A WAY OUT!

BE CAREFUL!

THE NEXT DAY, JOHN GOES BACK TO ROBBEN ISLAND.

WHAT ARE YOU DOING HERE ON YOUR DAY OFF, JOHN?

I NEED TO SPEAK WITH MANDELA.

WHY?

I, UH, HAVE ORDERS TO SPEAK WITH HIM.

HE'S DOWN THERE.

THIS IS LIKE A HOLIDAY FOR THEM COMPARED TO THE QUARRY, DON'T YOU THINK?

IT IS NEVER A HOLIDAY WHEN YOU'RE A PRISONER.

WORTH A THOUSAND WORDS

> It had been a peaceful march. The children were told to disperse. They started singing *Nkosi Sikelele* [South African national anthem]. The police were ordered to shoot.
>
> — Sam Nzima, photographer

The South African police fired into the crowd of peaceful protesters on 16 June 1976. A young schoolboy named Hector Pieterson was one of the first to fall. Sam Nzima took the picture of Hector as his body was carried away.

All over the world, people were angry. The picture said it all. It became a symbol of the brutality of apartheid.

Sam Nzima's newspaper, *The World*, was shut down by the government because of this photograph. Nzima had to move away from Soweto because the police were after him.

In 2002, the Hector Pieterson Museum opened its doors. Hector's sister Antoinette, the girl in Nzima's picture, gives museum tours to honour her brother's memory.

FREE AT LAST

Nelson Mandela after his release from prison

By 1990, Nelson Mandela had been in prison for 27 years. President F.W. de Klerk finally ordered his release. It was part of his move to end apartheid.

On 11 February, Mandela walked free. Fifty thousand people lined the streets of Cape Town to see him as he left the prison. Television cameras showed the moment live to people all over the world.

When Mandela appeared, many were moved to tears. They saw a grey-haired man of 72 years! He had not been photographed since he was sent to prison as a young man.

A South African poet named John Matshikiza said later: "We'd been waiting all of our lives for this. That is all I can say. It was the whole of my life."

RAINBOW

In 1994, Nelson Mandela was elected president of South Africa. It was the first time in the country's history that non-whites were allowed to vote.

Mandela was the first black president of South Africa. When he took office, Mandela called South Africa 'a rainbow nation at peace with itself and the world'. He used the word rainbow to show that South Africa's future would be shaped by people of all colours together. It would not be just black or white.

The new government set up the Truth and Reconciliation Commission. Everyone who had suffered under apartheid was invited to tell his or her story so that it would be known. The Commission helped South Africans to heal from the wounds of the past.

NATION

Today, South Africans of all races live together in peace. There are still problems of poverty and disease. But people are no longer judged only by the colour of their skin.

Nelson Mandela stepped down as president in 1999. He still works for world peace and speaks out on behalf of those who suffer unfair treatment. He is a much beloved elder statesman of the entire world.

INDEX

GLOSSARY

apartheid – the collection of laws that were used in South Africa to treat people of different races differently

discriminate – to treat people differently or unfairly because of their race, beliefs, etc.

equal – to be valued the same as someone else

ethnic – typical of a particular racial group

injustice – lack of fair treatment

Nobel Prize – a prize given every year to people who have most helped humanity in specific subjects

prejudice – a bad opinion formed without looking at the facts fairly

protest – a statement or action showing that you don't agree with something

sentence – a punishment given to a convicted criminal